BRITAIN IN PICTURES
THE BRITISH PEOPLE IN PICTURES

BRITISH
HERBS AND VEGETABLES

GENERAL EDITOR
W. J. TURNER

The Editor is most grateful to all those who have
so kindly helped in the selection of illustrations
especially to officials of the various public
Museums Libraries and Galleries and
to all others who have generously
allowed pictures and MSS
to be reproduced

BRITISH HERBS
AND
VEGETABLES

GEORGE M. TAYLOR

*WITH
8 PLATES IN COLOUR
AND
27 ILLUSTRATIONS IN
BLACK & WHITE*

COLLINS · 14 ST. JAMES'S PLACE   LONDON
MCMXLVII

PRODUCED BY
ADPRINT LIMITED LONDON

PRINTED IN GREAT BRITAIN
BY JARROLD AND SONS LTD NORWICH
ON MELLOTEX BOOK PAPER MADE
BY TULLIS RUSSELL AND CO LTD MARKINCH SCOTLAND

LIST OF ILLUSTRATIONS

PLATES IN COLOUR

BLACK AND WHITE ILLUSTRATIONS

Woodcut, 1710

INTRODUCTION

With hand in hand to leade thee foorth,
To Ceres Campe, there to behold
A thousand things, as richlie woorth
As any pearle is woorthie gold.

THOMAS TUSSER, 1580

WE are particularly fortunate in having a wide selection of Vegetables and Herbs, and although many of them are introductions from abroad we have, nevertheless, some esteemed kinds that have been evolved through the course of years from native wild plants.

Vegetables have aroused intense interest during the last six years, and thousands of people who possessed gardens and had never cultivated a vegetable before had, of necessity, to learn how to grow them in order to supplement their food rations. That activity aroused a desire on the part of cultivators to grow other sorts than the hitherto somewhat stereotyped occupants of the pre-war kitchen garden and allotment, and a vigorous propaganda on the part of the authorities whetted the appetites of the growers with the result that many of them developed great enthusiasm and desired to try kinds they had not previously attempted.

The wild plants are dealt with fully in this book, but the exotic kinds shall be reviewed and their history summarised.

7

Our British native flora is notable for the wide range of plants that are of culinary value, and many of these are the foundations of many of our most popular vegetables to-day. In their pristine, or wild, state, they are particularly unattractive, but in the passage of the years they have been developed to an almost incredible extent by the skill and patience of man. I have been struck with the insistence of horticultural writers, when dealing with the history of cultivated vegetables, on our indebtedness to the Romans for practically all the fruits and vegetables that we enjoy to-day. I am not concerned here with fruits, but I am perfectly convinced that we had, growing wild on our own soil, many species which cultivation and selection on the part of our forefathers subsequently developed into the fine sorts now grown so extensively by professional and amateur alike.

It would be futile to attempt to arrive at the origin of many of our cultivated plants, and particularly so in the case of vegetables. To call some of them indigenous, therefore, may be entirely wrong, even although they have been cultivated, as well as being found growing wild, as far back as history records. The first cultivators of the soil, the men of the Neolithic age, came to our islands from the Continent: they were almost certain to have brought seeds of vegetables with them, including cereals, for food, and it is equally certain that the seeds of weeds would be mixed with the crop seeds which they brought with them to their new settlements. Our ancestors were nomads, perhaps, on the plains of Asia, and they migrated from the open steppes into forest-clad Europe. Open land was very limited, and they had to cultivate it or starve. They had to learn to till the soil.

Most of our vegetables are actually of great antiquity. Biblical references to them are numerous, particularly the sorts mentioned, for example, in the reigns of the Pharaohs. Some two thousand years ago, too, Pliny wrote extensively upon the vegetables of his era, and many other old writers followed his example. One thing is certain, and it is that prior to the foundation of Rome we have no earlier records of how these vegetables were produced, but when the environs of the Eternal City became established they were cultivated and market gardens sprang up. In those gardens, as we know from the writings of Cato, Varro, Columella, Pliny, Virgil, and Martial to mention a few only, were grown many of the vegetables which we find in gardens to-day. Many of the botanical names of the vegetables are derived from the surnames of the landed Roman proprietors who were responsible for the growing of them. There are, for instance, the Pisones, the Fabii, the Cicerones and the Lentulii—thus *Pisum*, the Pea; *Faba*, the Bean; *Cicer*, the Chick Pea; and *Lentulus*, the Lentil.

So, it will be noted, many records have been left of the Roman appreciation and cultivation of vegetables, and they receive the credit of having introduced many of them to us. We have improved the cultivation of those vegetables; we have produced superior varieties, but I think we have not added very greatly to the number of species in actual cultivation for use as

8

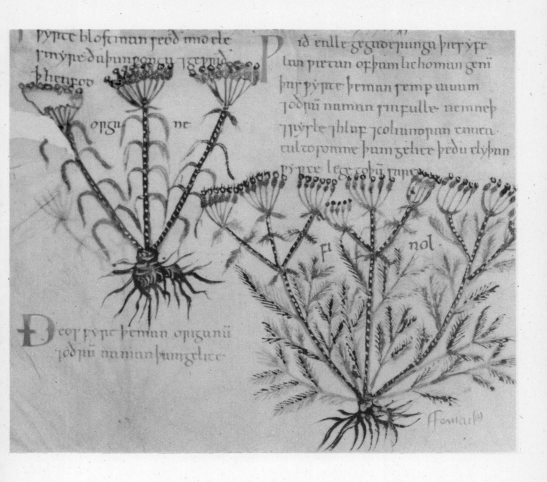

FENNEL

Detail from an Anglo-Saxon Ms. of the eleventh century

By courtesy of the Trustees of the British Museum

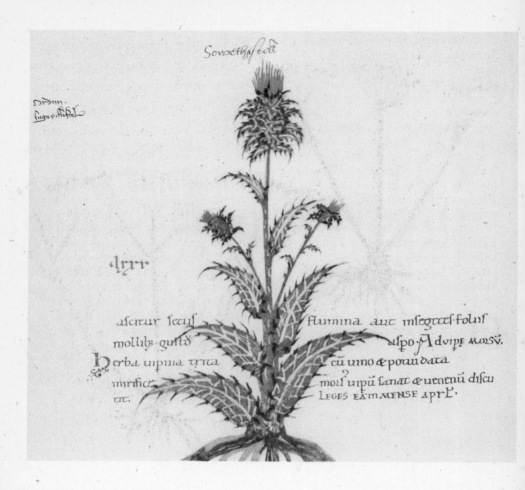

SOW THISTLE

Detail from the Ms. *Herbarium of Apuleius Barbarus* written in England, c.1100

By courtesy of the Curators of the Bodleian Library

food. Vegetable growing was a great art with the Romans. Where they went they took, amongst other things, their vegetables with them, and so it came that some of their favourites reached our shores and were planted for the benefit of tne new settlers and the armies of occupation. But, prior to the Roman invasion, what were our ancestors using in the way of vegetable food? We shall show that they had abundant vegetables and herbs long before the Romans reached this country.

The Roman Empire fell, and history is silent about vegetables or anything else for a long period. With the advent of the sixteenth century Gerarde, in his famous *Herball,* deals with and illustrates many vegetables grown in his day. The descriptions and illustrations are very quaint, and they demonstrate clearly that little improvement seems to have been made when we consider the long period during which vegetables had been under cultivation. A nostalgic preoccupation with the past is apt to give a prejudiced attitude to the present, but it may be remarked that during the seventeenth and eighteenth centuries there was an immense development. One point emerges from a study of some of the old literature on the subject of vegetables, and it clearly shows that many of our best sorts have been evolved from plants growing wild in our own country. How this work was accomplished in the old days is problematical; selection, no doubt, played a great part, but it is not until comparatively recent times that authoritative enlightenment is available.

RADISH
Woodcut from Gerarde's *Herball,* 1597

1. 'Skirrit'   2. Parsnip   3. Carrot
4. Turnip   5. 'Narewe'   6. Black Radish   7. Common Radish
Woodcut in 'The Kitchen Garden' from John Parkinson's *Paradisi in Sole*, 1629

AT THE MARKET
Detail from a loose-sheet woodcut
'Tittle-Tattle,' 1603

THE DEVELOPMENT OF OUR

WILD VEGETABLES

ALL horticulture, or the art of gardening, is relative to climate and purpose, and the climate has undoubtedly had a lot of influence upon the amelioration of vegetables of all kinds. History has demonstrated to us that so far as Europe is concerned, our own island, Holland, France, Germany, and the North of Italy are the best countries for European gardening, and their influence upon the development of gardening, and especially of vegetables, is proof of that claim. Britain has had a very large share in that work despite the alleged vagaries of climate. It is recorded that Charles II, a refugee for many years on the Continent after the battle of Naseby, said, in reply to some people who were reviling our weather, that he thought it was the best climate where he could be abroad in the air with pleasure or at least without trouble and inconvenience, the most days of the year, and the most hours of the day. Coupled with the skill of our gardeners of old, their undoubted knowledge—a lot of it empirical it may well be—of the art of selection, and aided by our climate, we have the basis of the gradual development of our vegetables in the many forms we grow to-day. Selection is the main factor in that development.

11

CABBAGES, BROCCOLI, CAULIFLOWERS AND TURNIPS, OR THE BRASSICAS

The name of this great genus is of Celtic origin. It comes from *bresic*, which means a cabbage. It is worth noting that the two chief divisions of Celtic Britons were the Gaels of Ireland and the North of Scotland, and the Cymri of Wales. The Caledonian Celts knew little about the Romans, hence the interest in the name now given to what is probably the largest and most popular group of culinary vegetables in cultivation to-day.

Brassica oleracea, the foundation of the whole cabbage race, is a native of this country, and is pre-eminently European. The genus embraces a large number of species which are distributed from the North of Europe down to the Mediterranean. *Brassica oleracea* is fairly general on the seashore at Dover, and on the rocks on the Glamorgan coast and in similar places around the country. I find it on the sand-dunes in my county of East Lothian. As will be noted later on, it is extraordinary that such a variety of forms so totally different in character should have originated from this humble wild plant, and there is scarcely another instance in the history of vegetables of a basic form producing such a great number of varieties. This wild plant is easily distinguishable when it is found amongst our native wildings. Its leaves are fringed, or waved, and are often tinted with red—cultivation produced the red pickling cabbage—and it sends up a flower-stem bearing a host of pale lemon-coloured flowers which seed profusely.

As we have already seen, the cabbage tribe is an outstanding instance of the combinations of genius and climate, and the variations resulting therefrom are extraordinary. The effects of the influence of climate are indelibly stamped upon the evolution of this genus, and it will be observed that the hardier forms, such as the kales and

CABBAGE,
CAULIFLOWER, KOHLRABI
From *Paradisi in Sole*, 1629

drumhead cabbages, originated and established themselves in northern regions, whereas the less hardy forms, such as the cauliflowers and the quick-growing sorts of cabbages, tend to the southwards. The great variety of hardy savoys, kales, brussels sprouts and the late varieties of hardy cabbages that are cultivated in the North were not found growing in the southern counties a century or two ago.

There's cauld Kail in Aberdeen,
And custocks in Strathbogie.

In the North of Scotland some years ago the principal vegetables of the cabbage type in general cultivation were the kales such as the green Borecole, or Scotch Kale, the German, or Curly, Kale, and the perennial kale with finely cut leaves. The latter, rarely seen now for it is an austere vegetable, was a favourite with the crofters before the better sorts were introduced. It was easily propagated by means of cuttings, and these were simply planted where they were to be grown for use. Its cultivation gave the minimum of trouble and saved its growers the annual cost of seeds. The plant is a true perennial like its ancestor *(B. oleracea)* and rarely bears flowers.

The custocks, which are the soft piths of the kale stalks, were in common use in the North. In the South the cauliflowers and the smaller type of cabbages were largely grown and also broccoli. Cauliflower was a great favourite. Dr. Johnson said: "Of all the flowers in the garden, I like cauliflower."

The type plant *(B. oleracea)* is a true perennial and not a biennial as contended by John Claudius Loudon, Dr. Neill, and other old authorities. Professor Salisbury records that a plant which he found wild on the rocks of the Glamorgan coast bore over five thousand seed-pods, with an average of fourteen apparently good seeds in each—a potential progeny of over seventy thousand! From such a wild plant as that we have obtained all the forms of cabbages, kales, cauliflowers, and broccolis that are now in cultivation.

There is no record to show how all the many distinct forms that now exist originated, and it is impossible to tell whether they were developed direct from the native plant or whether one type was eventually developed from another. There is evidence, however, to show that when mutation had begun—and remember that climatic conditions had a great deal to do in exciting that factor—it

CABBAGE
Detail from John Parkinson's
Paradisi in Sole, 1629

13

was quickly observed by keen growers and new types became stabilised and were improved by selection. This work must have extended over a long period, two or three centuries at least, and great care must have been taken in carrying it out. Brassicas are an adulterous race, and if any two forms are seeded near to each other the results are disastrous and the plants so obtained lose their individuality completely. This ease in inter-crossing would seem to confirm the belief that the diverse forms so obtained point to a common origin. In the seed-growing districts of the country to-day, in Essex for example, one of the problems confronting the seed grower is the isolation of a block of any of the cabbage that is intended for seed. It must never be close to another: unless steps are taken to prevent cross-pollination the seeds would be worthless. Their progeny would simply be an army of nondescripts.

As the wild plant was cultivated and seed sown from generation to generation, and a host of new types began to appear, the best of them and also the most distinct were isolated and grown on for further improvement. In the seventeenth and eighteenth centuries there were many market gardens in the environment of London, and there can be no doubt regarding the skill of the men who cultivated them. Abercrombie (1755–1806) tells us a lot about those gardens in his gardening books, and at the middle of last century, Charles McIntosh, famous gardener to the King of the Belgians at his British residence of Claremont, and afterwards gardener to the Duke of Buccleuch at Dalkeith Palace (the gardens there being at that time— 1850—amongst the greatest in Europe), wrote in his *Book of the Garden* some appreciative remarks regarding the London market gardens. He gave full details of the practices carried out in those places and maintained that the men who tilled them were the best culinary gardeners in the world, and that it was a subject that was scarcely hinted at by authors on gardening since the days of Abercrombie. A great deal of space is devoted in McIntosh's book to the excellent modes of culture carried out in the old gardens, and he considered that young gardeners would acquire a much greater amount of useful information in the general routine of their pro-fession were they to spend a year in a first-rate London market garden, than they could do in a dozen years, toiling nearly as hard, in very inferior places in the country.

It was in such gardens that vegetables were improved from year to year by careful selection on the part of the growers, and although those gardens were not alone in that particular work, they certainly had a major share in it. Edinburgh was also the centre of a clever colony of market gardeners, and the rich soils extending from Musselburgh to Dunbar produced some splendid improvements on the old types of cabbages.

Cauliflowers as we know them to-day, are divided into several distinct types. It may be that we obtained the first of them from Cyprus or some other part of Southern Europe on the shores of the Mediterranean from around the Bay of Naples, or from France, but at one time, probably about the end of the seventeenth century, English growers took a hand in the improvement of this vegetable. Dr. Neill, writing in the horticultural supplement to the *Edinburgh Encyclopaedia* and the *Appendix* to the *Encyclopaedia Britannica*, over one hundred and fifty years ago, said that cauliflower could then be claimed to be an English product, and till the time of the French Revolution quantities of English cauliflower were sent regularly to the Low Countries, and that even France depended on us for cauliflower seed. He records that for the early supply of the London market, very great quantities of cauliflower were fostered under handglasses during winter and the first part of spring: and that to behold some acres overspread with such glasses, gave a forcible idea of the riches and wealth of the metropolis.

The Dutch, with characteristic enterprise, took up the cultivation of cauliflower for themselves, and along with

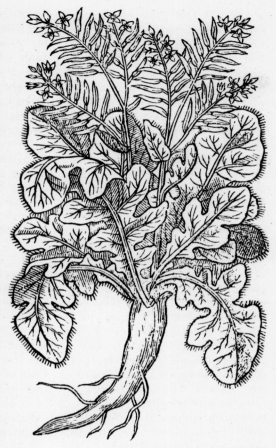

WILD TURNIP
Woodcut from John Parkinson's
Theatrum Botanicum, 1640

Danish and German growers we had a northern type of this vegetable exemplified by such varieties as Erfurt and Snowball. They are mostly early maturing types, and are ready for cutting in advance of the southern or Mediterranean forms. They all differ considerably, but all emanate from the basic *B. oleracea* and have gradually conformed themselves to their climatic environment.

Broccoli in all its forms, sprouting and otherwise, comes from the same wild plant. As with cauliflowers, there is a very wide variation and there are green, white and coloured types in this class. We have varieties adapted

15

to the different parts of the country and suitable to the varying soil and climatic conditions. As to the origin of broccoli, Vilmorin, a distinguished French seed grower, thought that the sprouting broccoli represented the first form exhibited by the new vegetable when it ceased to be the earliest cabbage, and was grown for the benefit of its shoots. After that, by continued careful selection, varieties were obtained which produced a solid white head. Vilmorin's opinion has been confirmed by the experiences of some of the Scottish market gardeners who had exactly the same development from a type of cabbage to a sprouting broccoli. There is a similar record in England where Professor Buckman, of Cirencester, raised sprouting broccoli from seed of the wild cabbage. Broccoli may have originated in Italy as some authorities claim, but our home growers, in England and Scotland, have done and are still doing a lot of work to improve it and select types hardy enough for our varying climatic conditions. The vast number of forms derived from this humble wilding are almost incredible, and the food supply they have created is a valuable contribution to the alimentary resources of the country.

With the advance of our knowledge of cytology the workers in this field of research have made rapid progress in recent years, and the great Brassica genus is now divided into three groups each with a definite number of chromosomes. This has resulted in clarifying the relationship of the various forms that have so far been evolved. The first group consists of forms with eighteen chromosomes, and is as follows: Curly Kale, Dwarf Scotch Kale, Russian Kale, Cottager's Kale, Thousand-headed Kale, Perpetual Kale, Marrow-stemmed Kale, Hearting Kale, Ragged Jack Kale, the wonderful coloured variegated kales with their tints of pink, blue, red, yellow, white, etc., all the forms of Cabbage, Cauliflower, Broccoli, Brussels Sprouts, Savoys, Drumheads, Coleworts, and Kohlrabi. The second group has twenty chromosomes in its cells, and is confined to the Turnips—which we shall deal with later—and the third group which has thirty-eight chromosomes contains the Asparagus Kale, Hungry Gap Kale, Late Rape Kale, and the white and yellow Swede Turnips.

We have, then, some idea of the evolution of one of our most valuable vegetables, but, unfortunately, the cabbage portion of it has suffered very badly at the hands of the cook. André L. Simon, the great authority on such matters, in an article in the *Journal of the Royal Horticultural Society*, vol. LXVII, part 5, wrote: "No vegetable, and there is no more important vegetable dietetically, has been, is, and will probably continue to be ruined by cooks as the homely cabbage." He gives us the orthodox method of cooking cabbage as generally given in the form of recipes in the majority of cookery books, and maintains that such treatment reduces cabbage to mere roughage, robbing it of goodness and flavour and rendering it as uninteresting gastronomically as almost useless dietetically. He gives his way of cooking, and points out that cabbage is wholesome because it contains

VERBENA OR VERVAIN

Detail from an English Herbal of the thirteenth century

By courtesy of Professor Charles Singer and the Curators of the Bodleian Library

ASPARAGUS

Coloured engraving by Elizabeth Blackwell from her *Curious Herbal*, 1739

By courtesy of the Royal Horticultural Society

in addition to a large proportion of nitrogenous matter, a certain amount of sulphur, a deficiency of which is one of the most prevalent causes of poor resistance to many human ailments. Cabbage has been blamed for its nasty smell when cooking, but Simon asserts that the odour arises from the precious sulphur proclaiming its presence, and it is infinitely better to put up with a passing smell than to eat desulphurised cabbage. He also warns people about cabbage offered in some catalogues that are guaranteed to be free from all objectionable smell. He warns buyers about cabbage of that character and begs them not to plant them as they are no good to anybody. In regard to this smell and its elimination, Mr. Simon advises that it can be dealt with satisfactorily by putting a piece of stale crust in the pan when cooking. He contends that most of the steam and stink will make it their home and all will be well.

THE TURNIP

In regard to the question as to the origin of the cultivated Turnip, we need not occupy ourselves with the botanical limits of the species, and with the classification of the races, varieties and sub-varieties, since all the Brassicae are of European or Siberian origin and are still met with in the wild state in some form or another. *Brassica rapa, B. campestris* and *B. napus,* together with *B. oleracea,* which are the foundations of all our turnips, are all native plants. The popular name "neeps" is derived from the Anglo-Saxon word for the turnip, "neepa." There is no means of ascertaining what, if any, forms of the turnip as we know them to-day, originated in this country, but we do know that its cultivation has been practised from very ancient times and that it was well known to the Greeks and Romans. We also know that turnips were first grown in the neighbour-hood of London for culinary purposes about three centuries ago, and they soon extended to the fields as their food value for stock feeding became apparent. Norfolk appears to be the first county where they were extensively cultivated for cattle. The field cultivation of this vegetable extended very rapidly when the seeds were sown in drills. This system originated with Jethro Tull (*circa* 1731) who introduced many improvements into agricultural practice and who wrote some books on the subject. Farmers were very slow to adopt the drilling method, but the success of those who did soon led to a general adoption of it all over the country and it caused a revolution in farming.

Turnips are now divided into two main groups by the systematist. First, there is a group with twenty chromosomes in the plant cells, and which is made up of the Turnip Rape, the white-fleshed, yellow-fleshed, yellow Purple-top, and yellow Green-top kinds. Second, a group with thirty-eight chromosomes consisting of the Hungry Gap Kale, the Asparagus Kale and the Swede Turnips. It is now concluded that swedes have arisen from the hybridising between members of the other two groups of Brassicae already referred to, and that the yellow, or hybrid, turnips, are due to variations arising from forms within the eighteen- and twenty-chromosome groups. Although nothing really definite has been established in regard to origin, it seems probable that there is a connecting link between some of the cabbages—with eighteen chromosomes in their cells—and turnips. Great work in the selection and improvement of swede turnips as well as the garden kinds was done by English and Scottish farmers over the last two centuries, and as a result we now have the race of splendid white and yellow garden kinds that we enjoy to-day. They are small in size in comparison with the older kinds, but they are much more palatable and enjoyable. Then, in addition, there is the great race of swede turnips upon which our farmers rely for the feeding of stock. Scotland, in the first half of last century, did a lot in the improvement of this class of turnip, and many fine strains are grown in the North for seed to-day.

It is worth noting that in the county of Moray, up till about a century ago, on an island in a lake there, and in the county in general, the turnip was found more plentifully in a wild state than anywhere else in Britain. A fortress existed on the island, and amongst the ruins the turnips seeded themselves from year to year and spread locally. It is thought that the last crop, probably sown four to five hundred years ago by the occupants of the fort, was never gathered and the seedlings sprang up annually in a mass without culture. It is recorded that some of the seedlings had roots weighing about a pound each, but most of the plants resembled the wild kinds and had long thin roots. The original turnips in this locality must have been introduced from the Continent at a very early period, for their cultivation for the feeding of cattle was first introduced into Morayshire, from the county of Norfolk, about 1760.

The Morayshire wild colony of turnips and its reversion to the wild condition serves as an illustration of the necessity for careful annual selection of the best plants for growing on for the saving of seed. Unless that is done, degeneration is rapid and a stock, or strain, of any vegetable soon reverts to the wild type. Our fine strains of vegetables have all been evolved and their high standard maintained by the careful methods of selection carried out by the seed grower through generation after generation.

THE CARROT

When we consider the insignificant wild plant, *Daucus Carota*, which is the foundation of our present race of garden Carrots, and also the fact that it is a common poisonous wilding of no seeming importance, we can appreciate what has been done by patient cultivation and selection. The French and Germans grew carrots on a very large scale, not only for the

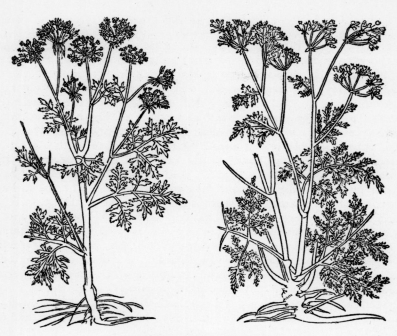

YELLOW AND RED CARROT
Woodcut from Henry Lyte's *Niewe Herball,* 1578

feeding of live-stock, but also for the manufacture of sugar and for distilling. We discovered the value of this vegetable during the war. It is very rich in saccharine matter. In the year 1833 the French horticulturist, M. Vilmorin, took the wild carrot in hand in an endeavour to improve it: he sowed seeds, selected the best of the progeny from year to year, and in four generations he succeeded in producing roots from the wild plants which must have been similar to those used in ancient times—for the carrot, in a very primitive form, has been cultivated for many centuries—and from which modern types have now been evolved. The roots, to begin with, were mostly white, but the coloured character appeared in the third generation, and was stabilised and made permanent by Vilmorin. The roots were inclined to be fibrous, but that undesirable trait was soon bred out. Our home seed growers now have some fine strains of their own of carrots of all types, from the modest stump-rooted kinds to the long-rooted varieties which are the pride of the exhibitor at the vegetable shows, and rigorous selection is maintained from year to year when seed saving is in progress. Improvements are still being made, and the hard core in the centres of the roots is being gradually eliminated. In this country we like the golden yellow sorts, but white and purple kinds are grown on the Continent.

As we know from Biblical history, the Israelites complained to Moses, after the exodus from Egypt, that they missed their Leeks, and we also know that this esculent was largely grown in that country in the days of the Pharaohs. Pliny, too, wrote that the best leeks were brought from Egypt. These references to the leek have led some of our older horticultural authorities to assume that the plant is a native of Egypt. Whatever the Egyptian leek may have been in that country, we now know that it is a very inferior vegetable to our own. During the years of the Great War leek seed was very scarce owing to the failure of our home-grown crops, and seed was imported from Egypt. Seed from that origin was a failure and poor crops of indifferent quality were the result. The finest, largest and hardiest of all our cultivated leeks is the one known as the Musselburgh. Imitation is the sincerest form of flattery, and the Musselburgh leek has many substitutes in commerce to-day and sophisticated strains are common. This vegetable appealed to the Scots and Welsh, but until quite recently it was in little request in England. The scarcity of onions, owing to lack of imports during the war, soon remedied matters and the culinary importance of the leek was recognised and appreciated by growers in the South.

In Scotland leek culture is a religion rather than an art. Musselburgh was, and still is, the centre of an able colony of market gardeners, and there is a tradition in the old burgh that some of their ancestors found the leek growing wild on the common waste land on the outskirts of the town. This ground was subsequently laid out as a golf course. Bearing that old tradition in mind, it is now accepted by botanists that *Allium Ampeloprasum* is the parent, or at any rate, the foundation of the leek, and that plant is a native of this country. It is also a common plant in the East and in the Mediterranean region. I myself have found it growing wild near Musselburgh. We have seen in regard to the Brassicas that hardy forms were developed in the North and less hardy forms in the South. The same experience undoubtedly applies to *A. Ampeloprasum*. Its development in Egypt would result in cultivated forms acclimatised to the climatic conditions of that country; its development in Scotland would result in types, culminating in the Musselburgh leek, that were adapted to our weather and by exposure to the elements it gained through time the hardy character that is now associated with it. Again, there is no historical evidence to show us how and when the leek originated in the many countries in which it is grown, and we can assume, as in the case of other vegetables, that the process was gradual through the centuries. One thing is certain, and it is that our home-grown strains of leeks of the Musselburgh type, are the finest in the world. Phillips, in his *History of Cultivated Vegetables,* informs us that the Welsh adopted the leek as their national badge, and they still continue to wear the emblem on St. David's Day in commemoration of a victory

20

they obtained over the Saxons in the sixth century, and which they attributed to the leeks they wore by order of St. David to distinguish them in battle. The Welsh patron died about the year 544. If that be correct, and there seems little reason to doubt it, the leek must have been cultivated long prior to that date. The leek, therefore, is a very ancient British vegetable, and the best strains or types in cultivation here to-day have undoubtedly been developed from a native wild plant.

The gradual improvement in the leek from the wild plant to the fine types now in cultivation, is an example of how most of our vegetables have been developed. Year after year seed was sown; the very best of the seedlings carefully conserved for growing on again for seed; the same process went on and is still going on. That is how the fine strains were built up and their superiority maintained. Mutations occasionally arose amongst the seedlings. Many of them were worthless, but some were improved forms and were isolated and cultivated by seminal methods. Seed growers pick out the finest examples of all the vegetables they are growing, and these are planted carefully for seeding from. Careful selection means progress.

THE ONION

The Onion is possibly the oldest culti-vated vegetable. Despite its antiquity its country of origin is still a mystery, but some authorities claim that it is a native of Baluchistan. It was a great favourite with the Egyptians, and the onions imported from that source in modern times are notable for their mild and juicy character. It is essentially a plant which requires the maximum amount of sunshine to develop it properly and to ripen the bulbs so that they may keep in good condition when stored. In the southern countries fringing the Mediterranean, in Tripoli, and other parts of North Africa, Spain, Portugal and Italy, this vegetable is grown in immense quantities for export and many of them come to this country. The date of the introduction of the onion to this country is not known, but it has been grown in British gardens as long as they deserve the appellation. The *Grete Herball,* printed by Peter

Woodcut from William Salmon's
Botanologia, 1710

21

Treveris in 1526, in describing this vegetable says:—"The Onion being eaten, yea though it be boiled, causeth headache, hurteth the eyes, and maketh a man dim-sighted, dulleth the senses, engendereth windiness, and provoketh over-much sleep, especially being eaten rawe. Being rawe, they nourish not at all, and but a little though they be boiled." As time went on the value of this vegetable as a tasty esculent began to be appreciated in this country, and it is now in great demand. It reigns supreme when we come to the question of flavour and appetite and in that respect it has the leek in close attendance. We now have many fine types of onion that were all raised in this country ranging from the exhibition sorts such as Ailsa Craig and Cranston's Excelsior to the smaller and better-keeping kinds such as James' Keeping, a type raised one hundred and fifty years ago in Lambeth which is still a favourite, and was actually one of the first acclimatised sorts to be grown in Britain. Although we can grow splendid onions in this country, some of them very large and impressive, we have not the climate to produce the finely flavoured well-keeping bulbs that come from more favoured climates.

When amongst Alliums we may note that another member of the genus, *A. Schoenoprasum,* is actually the popular Chive. This plant is indigenous to many parts of the country, and is often found in meadows and pastures.

The Shallot, *A. ascalonicum,* is indigenous to Palestine, and is abundant in the neighbourhood of Ascalon, hence the specific name. It came to Britain in 1548, by whom or how we have no record left. It is a great favourite in cottage gardens. The Tree and Potato Onions are now seldom seen.

THE PARSNIP

The Wild Parsnip, *Pastinaca sativa,* is common in many parts of this country. It is an umbelliferous plant, growing four feet in height, with small yellow flowers. Its root system extends to a great depth. Visitors to vegetable shows often express astonishment at the length of the roots of the prize-winning parsnips. Writing of this vegetable in the *Memoirs of the Caledonian Society* in 1821, Dr. McCulloch mentions one named the Coquaine, the roots of which sometimes run four feet deep and generally average six inches in circumference on the upper portion. It is difficult to trace how the parsnip was developed, but Pliny wrote that they were brought from the banks of the Rhine to the tables of the Roman Emperors. Phillips, in his *History of Cultivated Vegetables,* asserts that if the wild parsnip is grown for two or three years successively in rich soil, and seed saved annually during that period, it will assume all the characters of the cultivated sort. McIntosh, the eminent Dalkeith gardener, in his *Book of*

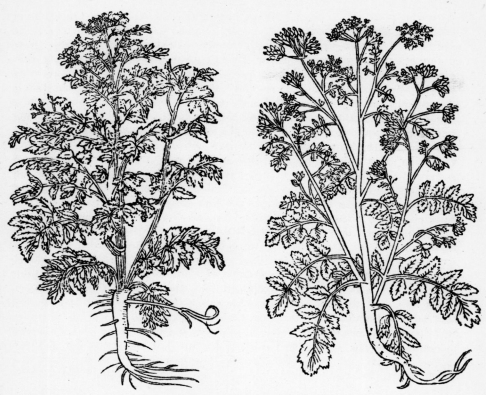

GARDEN PARSNIP AND WILD PARSNIP
Woodcut from Henry Lyte's *Niewe Herball*, 1578

the Garden, published in 1853, doubted that and considered it to be impossible, but the experiments of Professor Buckman confirm the statement made by Phillips. Buckman collected seeds of the wild form in 1847, and grew them and carefully selected them for a decade. In ten years he had produced a variety that was put into commerce under the name of "The Student" in 1861. That variety is still in cultivation and is offered in many seed catalogues. Great improvement has been made by our raisers since those days, and we now have excellent strains with shorter and thicker roots that are much more economical in use than the older types. The parsnip is a plant of great economic importance, and its value as such is not sufficiently appreciated. It is a very nourishing vegetable and our forefathers regarded it as an excellent substitute for the potato; the roots contain a high percentage of sugar; and at one time wine, which some authorities declared was equal to the Malmsey of Madeira, was made from it.

23

ASPARAGUS

Our native *Asparagus officinalis,* generally growing wild on some parts of our seashores, is also found on the salt-water steppes of Siberia, and it is a cultivated plant of great antiquity. It has been recorded as growing wild on the links fringing the seashore at Port Seton, East Lothian, about four miles from my home, but I have never found it there. The place is now a great picnic resort for people from Edinburgh, and the wild plants are rapidly disappearing. The elder Cato, writing about 200 B.C., appears to be the first to bring this vegetable into notice. He gave rules regarding its cultivation which are very sensible and are very much the same as those in favour to-day. Gerarde, in 1597, is the first English writer to describe Asparagus, and he calls it the "sperage" in his old herbal. He asserted that the Latin name "Asparagi" means "the first sprig or sprout of every plant, especially when it be tender." In *The English Gardener,* by Meager (1670), we are informed that the London market was well supplied with forced asparagus and are given details as to how it was grown. But asparagus appears to have been cultivated very largely in France and Austria, and it was a great favourite in the restaurants of Paris and Vienna. In its cultivated form it was probably introduced into this country about four centuries ago, and there is absolutely no evidence to show that any of our horticulturists actually developed it from the wild plant. That work must have been done elsewhere. As this vegetable began to come into favour in this country—after visitors to Paris and Vienna had had the opportunity of appreciating its goodness—our specialists began to give it attention and many fine forms raised in this country by seminal selection are now in commerce.

CELERY

In ditches and moist places in this country, one of the umbellifers named *Apium graveolens,* a rank, coarse weed, attaining a height of about four feet and with cauline, wedge-shaped leaves and umbels of insignificant flowers, is commonly met with. It is a most uninviting plant, and there is no record that it was ever used by man for food and even animals leave it severely alone. The country people called this weed "smallage." As a cultivated vegetable Celery began to appear in seed lists as "Upright Italian Celery," and it may be possible that we received it in that form from Italy. Many of the umbellifers have a very wide range, and the basic celery plant extends from Sweden to Algeria, Egypt, Abysinnia, and in Asia from the Caucasus to the mountains of India. It is a plant which has had a long period of cultivation through the centuries, and it is mentioned in the

COMMON WILD THYME

Coloured engraving from William Curtis's *Flora Londinensis*, 1798

By courtesy of the Royal Horticultural Society

TEASEL: SALSIFY: SOW THISTLE: VARIETIES OF WILD LETTUCE: DANDELION: CHICORY
BURDOCK: SAW WORT: COTTON THISTLE: HEMP AGRIMONY: TANSY
Coloured lithograph by J. E. Sowerby from C. P. Johnson's *The Useful Plants of Great Britain*, 1862

Odyssey, and by Theophrastus under the name of *selinon*. Later on, Dioscorides and Pliny distinguish between the wild and cultivated plants. It may be that we received the cultivated form from Italy, but our seedsmen and gardeners have raised many fine sorts, white, pink and red-stalked, during the last two centuries. Manchester was famous for its celery, and in the middle of last century celery from that neighbourhood held a leading place in the seed catalogues of those days. In the first decade of last century only four cultivated kinds were offered in catalogues, they were the common Upright Italian; the large Hollow-leaved Upright; the Solid stalked; and the large red-stalked Upright. In addition there was also Celeriac, or the Turnip-rooted Celery. It was a great favourite in Northern Europe, and the London market used to be supplied with it from the Continent about a century ago. The blanching of the stems, of course, is the explanation of the characteristic flavour of our cultivated celery. Our raisers have concentrated on raising kinds with fleshy stalks and with delicate flavour. Home-raised strains are now regarded as the finest in existence.

SALSIFY

We have two wild Salsifys in this country, but they are now somewhat rare. They are *Tragopogon porrifolius*—the leek-leaved salsify, and *T. pratensis*. The first is an inhabitant of moist meadows, and the other of common pastures. *T. porrifolius* is also a native of South-east Europe and Algeria. Parkinson tells us in his *Theatrum Botanicum* (1640) that T. *pratensis* was cultivated in gardens in his day, but it is now superseded by the leek-leaved species. Culinary authorities, however, say that both species are quite good and that there is little to choose between them. I can find no reference to the improvement of this vegetable by any of our growers, but cultivation would undoubtedly ameliorate the roots and gradually improve them in size and flavour.

SEA KALE

Sea Kale is one of our most delicious forced vegetables, and it has the merit of being easily cultivated and forced. When gardeners took this wild seaside plant, *Crambe maritima,* under their care, and how they became aware of its goodness, is not known, but although Gerarde knew it, his references to it are obscure and it was not until the days of Philip Millar, nearly a century and a half later than Gerarde, that we find definite reference to its culture and its uses. The etiolated stems produced by blanching are favourites with salad lovers, and are regarded as a great delicacy.

25

EXOTIC KINDS

THE POTATO

THE arrival of the Potato in this country marked a new epoch in our fields and gardens, and the position it created was second only in importance to wheat in its intrinsic merit as a food. There is no authoritative record as to how or when the potato was brought to Europe and subsequently to this country, but we do know that it was grown at Seville in 1570. From Spain it spread to Italy and to Belgium. Clusius, the celebrated botanist of the sixteenth century, received tubers in Vienna from Belgium, and published a description of the new plant in 1601 in his *Historia Plantorum*. But in 1597 our English herbalist Gerarde features the potato in his *Herball* and gives quaint illustrations of the plant and tubers. At that time it is obvious that more than one variety was in existence in Europe, because the potato of Clusius differed from that of Gerarde. The latter wrote that the potato prospered in his garden, and that would indicate that it had been grown there for some time previously. The generally accepted view of the introduction of the potato is that the tubers that were obtained by Gerarde were very probably got from the stores of one of Drake's ships which had picked up Hariot, Sir Walter Raleigh's representative and the leader of the Virginian colony, from Roanoke, and which landed them at Plymouth in 1586. Hariot, who was one of the foremost scientists of his day, brought over a collection of plants from Virginia, and the potato was included amongst them.

It was thought at one time that Raleigh actually brought the potato to England, but it is now known that he was never within two thousand miles of the South American indigenous potato, *Solanum tuberosum*, which is a native of Chile. Raleigh, no doubt, planted it on his estate at Youghal, in Southern Ireland, somewhere about 1588.

The potato made very little progress in this country until the middle of the eighteenth century. The main reason for the delay in popularity was that the open-field system of agriculture, which was in vogue over the major portion of the country at that time, did not allow crops to be garnered in the late autumn and that was a necessity in the case of the potato. The open-field system was caused by the right of pasturage, over the common arable fields, as soon as the corn was harvested. But in Scotland, in the North and West of England, as well as in Wales, where enclosure had long superseded the open field, the potato became popular in both field and garden at a much earlier date.

Our modern potato has a most remarkable versatility arising mainly from its innumerable varieties, and during the last century thousands of new kinds were raised from seed. Very few of them stayed the course after trial and they soon disappeared from cultivation. In England in 1656 it appears as if there were two distinct varieties in cultivation, and it was not until the end of the next century that improved kinds made their appearance. They were quite different from the sorts grown to-day; they were badly shaped and had large deep eyes. These undesirable traits have all been bred out of the tubers by patience and careful selection. In the last quarter of the eighteenth century a disease known as "curl" began to develop amongst potatoes in many parts of the country—it is a virus disease—and degeneration began to set in very rapidly. This stimulated the creation of new kinds, and thousands were raised in

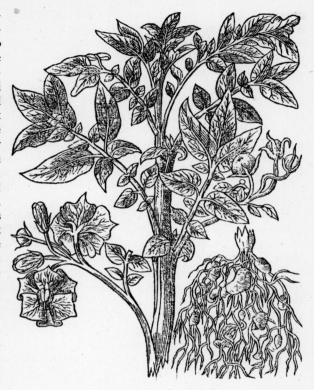

THE VIRGINIA POTATO
Woodcut from John Gerarde's *Herball*, 1597

an endeavour to create varieties that would withstand the trouble. Similarly, a fresh impulse was given to the raising of new sorts after the collapse of the potato crops in 1845 when a blight swept over the British Isles and Western Europe and devastated the crops. Emerging from the chaos caused by that disaster we had the famous varieties Paterson's Victoria, Sutton's Magnum Bonum, Nichol's Champion and Goodrich's Early Rose. The Champion was a very famous variety and it had grand quality and was highly resistant to disease. The consequence was that two-thirds of the acreage in Ireland, practically the whole of Scotland and the North of England was devoted to its cultivation. I have happy memories of the quality of this grand old potato.

Raisers had now something of a standard to work to, and many fine kinds began to appear. Breeding was stimulated by the appearance of a new disease in the first decade of this century. It was *Synchytrium endobioticum*,

27

popularly known as Black Wart. In consequence, fresh sorts became a necessity because most of our best potatoes were susceptible, but others were immune. The task of the raiser was to create others that were resistant to Black Wart embodying, at the same time, the virtue of good crops and fine quality.

Potatoes are divided into three sections, viz., Earlies, Second Earlies, and Maincrops. In all sections there are varieties that are adapted to certain soils and localities and they are chosen accordingly. For example, Majestic is a favourite in many counties in England; Kerr's Pink in the industrial parts of Scotland, King Edward in the South of England, and so on. Golden Wonder, which is recognised as being probably the best potato for quality, is a very poor cropper except on very good soils and for that reason it is not so largely grown as other kinds. But where quality is appreciated and good cultural conditions are afforded it is a supreme favourite.

Raisers have dealt with an attempt to eliminate Blight and Black Wart diseases by raising sorts that resisted those troubles, and they are now entering on another battle against virus. Certain Andean species have been found to be totally resistant to that wasteful disease, and they are now being used for breeding purposes. They were not previously used for that work because they would not cross with our domestic varieties, but science, through the development of cytology, has now enabled the potato breeder to overcome that difficulty. A species known as *S. Rybinii*—which has resisted all attempts to infect it with virus—has been successfully used for breeding, and a new variety named Dr. McIntosh will shortly be put into commerce. It gives great promise and has done well in all its trials. It crops heavily, has splendid quality, and has exceptionally vigorous growth.

We have now come to a period in potato development when, after assessing the accumulated results of careful and systematic breeding, the knowledge so obtained will enable growers to formulate fairly definite statements as to how to proceed to secure desired results. Considerable evidence, as well as fresh material, is already at hand, but on the whole the methods of breeding are still somewhat empiric. That phase, thanks to modern science, is now passing rapidly.

Plant breeding is worthy of the name only as it sets definite ideals and the worker is able to attain them. The mere production of new varieties is an action of no merit. The production of mere novelties, unless the new variety possesses some property which makes a real contribution, is simply a waste of time.

All our cultivated plants have come from wild forms, and man has seen in them the possibility of usefulness, and with the potato, as well as all our other vegetables, he has chosen year after year the ones which better serve his purpose. The constant selection that has gone on for generations has produced profound changes in our plants.

Pisum spontaneum nanum inter triticum, nobis.

*Auspiciis Nobilissimi & Honoratissimi
Iohannis Vicecomitis Mordaunt·*

DWARF PEA
Engraving after Francis Barlow from Robert Morison's
Plantarum Historiae Universalis Oxoniensis, 1715

PEAS

The Pea, as we know it to-day, is a very highly developed vegetable and is certainly one of the most appreciated, and it may well be when its high protein content is considered. We have several forms of wild peas and vetches in this country, but not one of them has any part in the upbuilding of the present forms. *Pisum maritimum*, a species which is indigenous to some parts of our sea coasts, is recorded as having been used for food in the great famine of 1555, and is credited as having been responsible for the saving of many lives at that time. The peas that are found in its pods have a very bitter flavour and are of no use in these days.

The date of the introduction of the edible pea into this country is un-known, but there are several forms of wild peas ranging through Southern Europe to Asia. It is a vegetable of very great antiquity for it was culti-vated by the Greeks and Romans in the time of Pliny. The French excelled in the cultivation of peas and so did the Dutch, but our modern varieties, evolved no doubt from these sources, are supreme. There are two distinct types in cultivation, viz., round and wrinkle-seeded, and there are dwarf, medium and tall-growing sorts in each section. The wrinkle-seeded peas are called Marrowfats and are esteemed for their delicious flavour. They are best used in a young state, and if peas are required for drying and storing the blue round-seeded kinds are best for the purpose. The latter part of last century saw the foundation of the fine strains of peas that are now so extensively grown, and at that time notable varieties were Prince of Wales, Ne Plus Ultra, British Queen, Telegraph, Veitch's Perfection and Advance. They are still in cultivation, but the work of raising new and improved forms has been continued and in all sections, dwarf, tall, round and wrinkle-seeded, we have now some remarkably fine kinds. The seed growers take infinite pains in the growing and selection of the plants that are to bear seed, with the result that the noted superiority of British strains of this vegetable are maintained and elevated.

BEANS

The spectacular Scarlet Runner Bean is probably the most popular bean in cultivation, and is grown in most gardens in the South of England and the Midlands. It is a native of South America and came to this country in 1633, and on its introduction, and for many years thereafter, it was simply regarded as an ornamental plant. In the first decade of the eighteenth century its value for culinary purposes was recognised, and when it began to become popular it was taken up by the plant breeder and gradually im-proved. Their main purpose was to improve the length and quality of the pods, and as a result we have the fine sorts such as Streamline and Scarlet Emperor which have pods twenty inches and over in length.

The so-called French Beans, or Dwarf Kidney, originally came to us from Southern Asia, via Holland, about the first decade of the sixteenth century. In the days of Queen Elizabeth they were called "Roman" beans. The first variety was called White Dutch. On the Continent they are called Haricot Beans. Gerarde, in his old *Herball,* writes: "The fruit and pods of kidney beans, boyled together before they be ripe, and buttered, and so eaten, with the pods, are exceedingly delicious meate." This is a vege-table which has undergone great improvement by our plant breeders, and some splendid kinds are now grown for use in the orthodox manner and also, after ripening, for use as haricots.

The Broad Beans are not now so extensively used as they were at one time. They were grown in prehistoric times in Arabia and Egypt, and some authorities regard them as being natives of the Caspian Sea area and North Africa. The date of their introduction into this country is not known. There are three types in cultivation. These are the Windsor, or Broad-podded; Longpod, with large, somewhat slender long pods; and the Mazagans with small seeds. The food value of the broad beans is very high if the seeds are used in a young state. When they are allowed to become large and have developed a "black eye," they are very austere and unpalatable.

TOMATOES

Some time in the fifteenth century another species of the genus Solanum was introduced into Europe from South America. It was *S. lycopersicum* from which our race of modern Tomatoes was evolved. Like the potato it has now become one of the most important and largest-grown vegetables. In 1597 in the days of Gerarde its fruits were very rough and corrugated, and all the old Herbals describe it as being unwholesome and having ill effects upon those who consumed it. In the course of time its value was gradually recognised, and during the latter part of last century it began to be appreciated by those who grew it. The plant breeder began to take it in hand and very soon improved it; types with different-sized fruits were obtained and smooth kinds were selected; early maturity was developed; and then sorts

LOVE-APPLE OR TOMATO
Woodcut from William Salmon's *Botanologia,* 1710

31

were introduced that had solidity of flesh, small seed vessels, and fine flavour.

The work went on intensively for half a century, and by selecting and breeding from the best kinds we see the result in the many excellent sorts in cultivation to-day. The yellow-fruited kinds are neglected, which is a pity because many people know nothing about them and have only grown and tasted the red-skinned varieties. Those who know the yellow-fruited tomatoes are emphatic in declaring that they are unsurpassed in flavour and are much superior in that respect to the red sorts. Apart from the large-fruited varieties that are generally grown, there are a number of small ones having fruits that resemble currants, cherries, pears and plums. Although they are very decorative they are of little use for eating, but some people use them in salads.

During the last few years a bush type has been introduced. The plants are dwarf and sturdy and require no staking. They are much favoured by some cultivators for out-door culture.

CUCUMBERS AND MARROWS

The Cucumber, *Cucumis sativus,* is actually amongst the oldest of culti-vated plants. It was introduced here in 1573 from North-west India, but it is a plant of nearly as great antiquity as the Vine. Cucumbers were favoured in the days of Moses, and the Emperor Tiberius required them to be served at his table every day. Like the tomato, it was a considerable time after its introduction into this country that cucumbers were cultivated to any great extent. The plant is a tender annual and requires great care to grow it satisfactorily. Again, like the tomato, the cucumber has established a considerable horticultural industry, and tons of them are sent every day to the London markets alone. They are grown, of course, in suitable heated houses or frames, but over a century ago in Hertfordshire, whole fields could be seen covered with cucumbers without the protection of glass. The produce was principally used for pickling. The noted market-garden town of Sandy, in Bedfordshire, was reputed to have sent 10,000 bushels of pickling cucumbers in one week to London. They would be the kinds we now know as Ridge Cucumbers. They are cultivated in the open. The larger and more refined sorts such as Telegraph and Matchless require to be grown in heat.

The native country of our cultivated Vegetable Marrow is not known, and the date of its introduction is obscure. The marrow has undergone great improvement during the last half-century, and there are now some choice kinds in commerce. We have green and yellow sorts in various shapes. The round, golden-skinned, kinds are very choice, and if the fruits are cut and used when young and tender they are delicious.

BEETROOT

Although we have a wild form of Beet-root, *Beta maritima,* in this country, it is very questionable if it has had any influence upon the sorts in present-day cultivation. They are probably descended from *B. vulgaris,* which is a native of Southern Europe. It has fleshy roots in the wild state, whereas our wilding has a very poor root system. That, however, is no reason why it should not have been developed satisfactorily, for we know from our experience with other examples of wild culinary plants that some of them which have slender roots in nature, easily become fleshy-rooted by cultivation or soil. The famous French seed grower, M. Vilmorin, proved that beet is easily improved by selection. The ancient Greeks and Romans cultivated beet to a great extent, and there is evidence that it was introduced into this country in 1546. The roots of our native wild beet are not eaten, but the leaves were used as substitutes for spinach. The white-rooted forms of *B. vulgaris,* in its selected and cultivated sorts, are now extensively grown in this and other countries for the production of sugar.

RED BEET OR BEETROOT
Woodcut from Henry Lyte's
Niewe Herball, 1578

HORSE RADISH

The Horse Radish, *Cochlearia Armoracia,* is a very doubtful native of this country. English botanists mention it as a wild plant, but the probability is that it was introduced here many centuries ago and has escaped from gardens. Babington, in his *Manual of British Botany,* second edition, mentions only one place where it is found wild, in the vicinity of Swansea. It is a plant which is indigenous to the temperate regions, and especially the eastern regions, of Europe. It is found from Finland to Astrakhan. The fact remains that it is a rare wild plant in our country. When once horse radish has been planted it is a very difficult subject to get rid of, and any bits thrown out soon root and establish themselves. Propagation and cultivation have naturalised the plant, and when it is grown under proper

33

conditions its flavour benefits accordingly. Gerarde tells us that horse radish was found growing wild—"at a small village neere London, called Hogsdon" by his "verie good friend Master Bradwell," who gave him "knowledge of the place where it flourisheth to this day." Gerarde's quaint assessment of the value of this vegetable is worth repeating. He wrote: "This kinde of sauce doth heate the stomacke better, and causeth better digestion than mustard."

SPINACH

Spinach comes from the wild *Spinacea oleracea*. There may be some doubt as to this plant, which is one of annual duration, being a native, and its cultivation in this country cannot be traced beyond 1568, but it was probably grown here long before that date. It has large leaves, hollow stems, and the flower spikes rise to a height of about three feet. It must not be confounded with the plant popularly called Wild Spinach. That is *Chenopodium Bonus-Henricus*, or, as it is known to country people, Good King Henry. That plant is indigenous to many parts of Britain, particularly on loamy soils in waste places. It is a perennial, and while young and tender, the leaves were used as a substitute for spinach. In some parts of the country it was actually preferred to spinach, and one old writer declares that the young shoots, peeled and boiled, may be eaten as asparagus. It is, nevertheless, an excellent spinaceous plant for cottage gardens and is very easily cultivated.

LETTUCE

Our excellent salad the Lettuce is a plant of very great antiquity. According to Herodotus it was cultivated over five centuries B.C., but Pliny writes that the Romans only knew one sort. Gerarde is the first to describe lettuce in this country, and he mentions eight sorts that were grown in his day. The names of the earliest cultivated kinds would seem to indicate that they came to us from the Greek islands—"Cos," for example. In any case, as with most other vegetables, the lettuce was considerably improved by our own horticulturists, and most of the best forms in cultivation to-day are certainly the work of our home specialists. We have three wild forms of the lettuce in this country, viz., *Lactuca elongata*, *L. saligna* and *L. virosa*, and it cannot be definitely stated which one is the basic plant of the cultivated forms. The exotic *L. scariola* var. *sativa*, a native of temperate and Southern Europe, and of the Canary Isles, Algeria, and of Eastern Asia, is undoubtedly the parent of some of the forms which we cultivate to-day, but it is equally evident that our native *L. virosa* has some influence in the upbuilding of the types now in cultivation in our gardens.

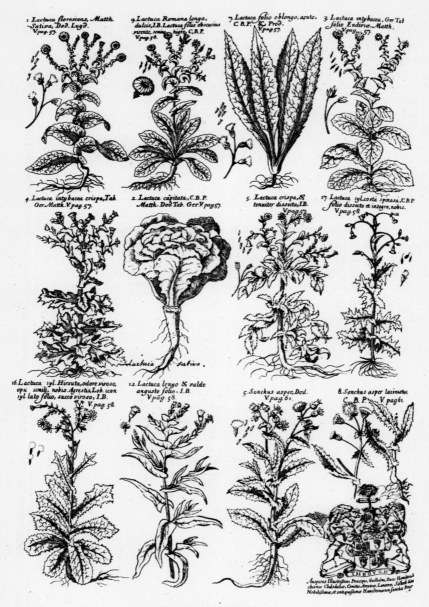

VARIETIES OF LETTUCE
Engraving after William Sonmans from Robert Morison's
Plantarum Historiae Universalis Oxoniensis, 1715

Lettuce abounds in a white milky juice which is highly narcotic, and at one time it was largely used as a substitute for opium. In the second decade of last century a celebrated medical man, Dr. Andrew Duncan, Senior Professor of the institute of Medicine of Edinburgh University, devoted a lot of time and experiment to the uses of the juices obtained from lettuce. He discovered that it could be used with effect in cases where opium was inadmissible. Full and interesting details are given of his work in that respect in the *Memoirs of the Caledonian Horticultural Society,* vols. I, II, and IV.

PARSLEY

This gracious herb came to us from Sardinia in 1548. Our old authority Gerarde waxes eloquent over its virtues and rightly so. Its value was known in the days of Pliny who tells us that no sauce or salad was ever served without it. It is now recognised as an excellent tonic, and a parsley sandwich will do the work of an iron tonic more cheaply and agreeably. The plant is a hardy biennial and became so common that it was found naturalised in many parts of this country. The original form, *Apium petroselinum,* is a poor thing in comparison with the fine curled sorts that have been bred from it.

PARSLEY
From *Hortus Sanitatis,* 1491

NEGLECTED WILD SPECIES

*Much food is in the tillage of the poor; but there
is that is destroyed for want of judgment.*
PROVERBS xiii. 23

O NE of our eminent old horticultural thinkers and writers has declared that all vegetables not absolutely poisonous may be rendered edible by proper preparation, and that it may be worth while for man in his present multiplied and highly civilised state, to reflect on these things, with a view to resources in times of famine. We know that in years of scarcity in olden times, the leaves of birch, beech, willow, gooseberry and others, were eaten as salads. That noteworthy economic individual the Scottish Highlander, for example, was reputed to have chewed the roots of the Mouse Pea, *Orobus tuberosus,* as a substitute for tobacco, and the equally frugal Hollander served the roots up as we do chestnuts after drying and roasting them.

Dr. Neill has recorded that the common weed of our hedgerows, *Erysimum alliaria,* or Jack-by-the-Hedge to give it its colloquial name, when gathered as it approaches the flowering stage, and if boiled separately and added to mutton, improves the flavour. He also says that it is good in combination with any salted meat, and is an excellent green.

We have a most neglected wilding in our well-known Willow Herb, *Epilobium angustifolium,* now so common almost everywhere and one of the most invasive of our native plants. Not only were the young and tender shoots eaten as asparagus, but the leaves were regarded as a wholesome green vegetable. Let any doubter try the young shoots of this plant in spring—they must be used in that stage—cut them as you do asparagus, and use in similar fashion. It is much appreciated in some parts of North America.

Another weed which is little short of a pest in some gardens is the Shepherd's Purse, *Thlaspi bursa-pastoris.* Correa de Serra, writing in the *Horticultural Transactions,* vol. IV, 445, declares that this plant varies considerably in the size and succulence of its leaves, according to the nature and condition of the soil in which it is grown. He mentions that in gardens near Philadelphia, this plant develops a size and succulence of leaf that is almost incredible if it were not apparent. When properly grown and blanched it is a valuable addition to the list of delicate culinary vegetables. It is also recorded that when it is boiled it has the flavour of cabbage, but it is softer and milder to the palate. Here, then, is a hint to those who do not like the harsh flavour sometimes found amongst cabbages. Why not try a few cultivated plants of the Shepherd's Purse?

The Chickweed, *Stellaria media,* too, was regarded as a delicacy and particularly so in spring when the leaves are young and tender. It was boiled and also eaten as a salad. I mentioned that to a man who, I noticed, was growing a fair crop of it in his garden, and I asked him if he used it. The reply was, no, I grow it for my poultry as I notice they prefer it to lettuce. Growing wild, often amongst the rubbish of old buildings, our native *Chenopodium urbicum,* the Fat Hen of the English country folks, was wont to be boiled and used as we now eat spinach. It was stated by old gardeners that it was by no means inferior to that vegetable.

The Garden Cress, *Lepidium sativum,* is not a native plant, and although we have three indigenous members of the genus I can find no reference to their being cultivated for salads. The so-called American Cress, *Barbarea praecox,* is a native of Britain and is a plant which is particularly fond of moist places. It was in great request at one time as a winter cress and early spring salad. *Barbarea vulgaris,* the Yellow Rocket, also common in moist places, was a favourite at one time. To-day it is seldom grown and I have only seen it in one garden whose owner appreciates its qualities and its pungent flavour. Our native Water Cress, *Nasturtium officinale,* seems to have ousted the Barbareas from favour. It is worth noting that the water cress does best in a stream whose current is not too rapid. In swift flowing water the leaves tend to become somewhat large and coarse and they then

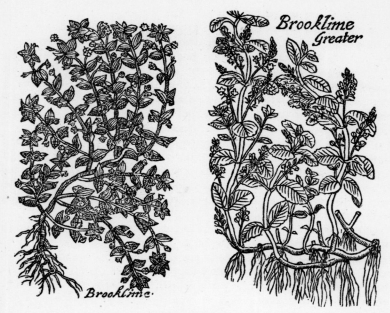

BROOK LIME
From William Salmon's *Botanologia*, 1710

resemble those of the Water Parsnip, *Sium angustifolium*, which is almost poisonous. There are many cress beds in the vicinity of London, and I remember the extensive ones at Tewin Water, in Hertfordshire. In the old days people who were fond of salads used to mix the leaves of the Brook Lime, *Veronica Beccabunga*, with the water cress, and they considered that the combination produced a more pleasing flavour. In Scotland sprigs of this plant were sold under the name of water purpie. It was only in 1808 that water cress was first marketed in London, and then only on a very small scale.

The Samphire, *Crithmum maritimum*, seems to be used only in districts where it abounds in the wild state such as rocky cliffs on the seashore. I first saw it in the fish shops at King's Lynn, in Norfolk, and again at Totnes, in Devon, and found on inquiry that it was used as an addition to salads to which it contributed a crisp, aromatic flavour. It is said to make an excellent pickle. The Golden Samphire, *Inula crithmifolia*, another sea-shore plant, was much used for the same purpose as the common samphire.

The Marsh Samphire, *Salicornia herbacea*, also plentiful near the sea, was used for salads and pickling.

The Cuckoo-pint, *Arum maculatum*, a common native plant, plentifully adorned with red berries after its flowers have faded, would hardly be

39

suspected of being an edible subject. But at one time its roots, which are about the size of a nutmeg, were in great request in rural districts where it abounded. The roots, after being thoroughly dried, were ground into a powder which was sent to London and sold under the name of Portland Sago. Some people used to consider that the berries of this plant were poisonous, but that is not the case. They are greedily devoured by birds. Another native plant whose roots are edible is *Orchis Moni*, an occupant of meadows and pastures in many parts of the country. A preparation called "salep" was made from the roots, but they were imported from Turkey in preference to our home-grown ones. The powder obtained from the roots was reputed to be highly nutritious as it contained a great quantity of farinaceous matter in small bulk. Another native Orchis, *O. mascula*, which is quite often met with in my locality, was also used for the same purpose as the other, and the produce from its roots was said to equal that of the imported material.

Spiraea filipendula, the Dropwort, a very common plant in pastures and a near relative of our Meadow Sweet, *S. ulmaria*, was a favourite in Sweden where its tubers were dried, ground and baked into bread. There is no record of its being used for edible purposes in this country. That curious little weed frequenting some of our pastures, the Earth-nut, *Bunium bulbo-castanum* was used in times of food scarcity and its tubers were eaten raw. They were considered to be a great delicacy; they are very sweet and have the reputation of being most nourishing. The Burdock, *Arctium Lappa*, one of our perennial weeds, produces stalks which were boiled and eaten as we now do asparagus. The Black Byrony, *Tamus communis*, common in our hedges through which it twines, was reputed to be a highly poisonous plant, but folks used to gather the young tops in spring and eat and enjoy them.

The Silver Weed, *Potentilla anserina*, with its golden blossoms and white foliage, also a native of our meadows, was greatly valued at one time for its roots. They taste like parsnips, and were greatly favoured at one time in Scotland when they were boiled or roasted. In some of the remote islands on the west coast of Scotland such as Jura, where food was often scarce, the roots of this plant actually supported the population when bread was unobtainable. Geese are very fond of the foliage of this plant and devour it with avidity. If this plant had been developed in the same way as the parsnip, we might now be enjoying another appetising vegetable. No doubt, in their pristine state, some of these wildings may be austere and somewhat harsh to modern palates, but had they been taken in hand by our vegetable growers they would almost certainly have become good culinary plants. I think full advantage has not been taken of them by growers.

The Nettle, *Urtica dioica*, commonly known as the Great Nettle, was much used at one time and even to-day some people make a practice of gathering leaves and using them for food. When the young tops of this plant begin to appear in early spring, they are collected for use in soups and

VEGETABLE MARROWS
Water colour by S. M. Fisher, 1945

SPROUT PICKING, MONMOUTHSHIRE

Oil painting by Evelyn Dunbar, 1945

Crown Copyright Reserved

they are also eaten in the same way as spinach. It is a plant that is very amenable to forcing, and if the roots are lifted, boxed or potted up, and grown in a warm place, the tender growths can be gathered in abundance. They were used at one time in severe winters, after the frost had destroyed the cabbage crop, for boiling as a substitute for green vegetables. In my district the leaves are still gathered by some of the country folks and used in the making of soup.

Mention must be made of our native Heather, *Calluna vulgaris*, and although we know that it is a plant of great economic importance to the Highlanders, it was used long ago for the making of what was said to be a most delicious beverage. Heather was very largely employed at one time for a multitude of purposes; the Highlanders used it for the thatching of their houses: for making their beds: for dye for their kilts and clothes: for tanning and making besoms. History tells us of the wonderful Heather Ale that was one of the luxuries of the Picts, and Gaelic literature and tradition are full of the excellence and potency of this beverage. The recipe for its manufacture is lost, but it can be imagined that a plant which yields such a delicate honey, would be very likely to produce an attractive drink. It is a conspicuous plant capable of developing great sweetness, and the bees may have taught man that there was more in it than honey.

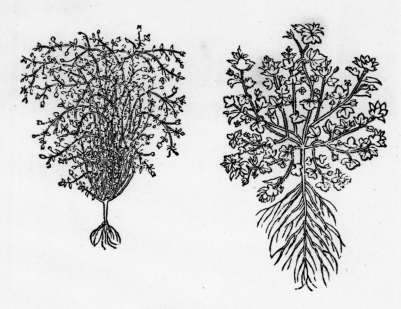

VARIETIES OF CHICKWEED
Woodcuts from Henry Lyte's *Niewe Herball*, 1578

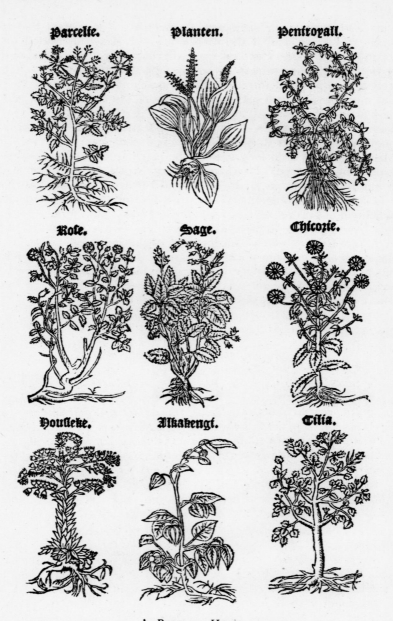

Parcelie. **Planten.** **Penirovall.**

Rose. **Sage.** **Chicorie.**

Houlleke. **Alkakengi.** **Tilia.**

A Page of Herbs
Woodcuts in the 'Index of the Book of Simples'
From William Bullein's *Bulwark of Defence against all Sickness*, 1562

GARDENERS
Woodcut from the title page of the *Grete Herball*, 1526

HERBS AND THEIR USES

NATIVE AND EXOTIC

*Culinary and afterwards medicinal herbs were the object of
every head of a family; it became convenient to have them
within reach, without seeking them at random in woods,
meadows, or on mountains, as often as they were wanted. When
the earth ceased to furnish spontaneously all these primitive
luxuries, and culture became requisite, separate enclosures for
rearing herbs became expedient. Fruits were in the same pre-
dicament and those most in use, or that demand attention, must
have entered into, and extended the domestic enclosure. Thus
we acquired kitchen gardens, orchards and vineyards.*

On Modern Gardening, 1770.   HORACE WALPOLE

IF the first vegetable production that attracted man was the fruit of
some tree, such as the Fig, the first herbage to be used would be the
succulent leaves and stalks which grew in abundance all around him. All
over this country there are plants in the wild state that are eatable and
nourishing. The Herb and Physic Gardens of the past paved the way to
a wider gardening. The Herb Gardens have now practically disappeared,
but during the last few years they have been again taken up by some people

WILD MINT
From John Parkinson's
Theatrum Botanicum, 1640

who have begun to recognise their value. About the second decade of last century there was a noted Herb Garden at Croydon; the owners cultivated about five hundred species, and the collection included practically the whole of the plants mentioned by Culpepper and other noted herbalists of the seventeenth century. There were many customers in those days, and there was a big demand from doctors, and also from quacks and irregular practitioners. In Scotland, Bishop Leslie, writing about 1578, of his tour through that country, said of Glasgow—"verie faire situatione and pleasand," and mentioned that it is abundant "in gairdine herbes, aiple trees, and orchardis." The oldest Physic Garden in Scotland was at Edinburgh, for in the year 1699 the King's Garden at what is now the Palace of Holyrood House became such a place, and it was the oldest of its kind in Great Britain after the one at Oxford which was founded in 1632. The Scottish Garden was the foundation of the famous Royal Botanic Gardens at Edinburgh. The Herbs, or "Simples," have thus a great influence upon modern gardening, and in these more enlightened days it is good to know that their value is being understood. Some herbs have a high vitamin content and are most valuable for cooking either in the form of salads or boiled.

It is quite impossible to deal here with all our native herbs: many of them are almost indispensable in medicine: others are invaluable in the economic sphere and are used for many purposes in modern commerce. I am only mentioning our native herbs which are useful for culinary work.

The Burnet, *Poterium Sanguisorba,* an indigenous perennial, which is common on calcareous soils, was in great request for use in salads and was a favourite for adding flavour to various drinks. Fennel, *Foeniculum vulgare,* is an old inhabitant of gardens, and its slender young stalks are used in salads: the leaves after being boiled are used for flavouring fish and other sauces. Borage, *Borago officinalis,* growing wild on waste places, in addition to being used as a salad was in great demand as a cordial herb for the

44

banishment of sorrow! There are several wild mints, but those principally cultivated are *Mentha piperita*, the Peppermint; *M. viridis*, the Spearmint; and *M. Pulegium*, the Penny-royal Mint. The Peppermint is used almost entirely for distillation and is largely grown for that purpose. Its produce enters into many medicinal prescriptions. The Spearmint, of which there are several forms, is used for making sauce. Penny-royal is also used for cooking and the making of Penny-royal water.

We have a wild Marjoram in this country, *Origanum vulgare*, but the Pot Marjoram which is in general use as a herb is a native of Sicily. It is called *O. Onites*, and the Sweet Marjoram, *O. heracleoticum*, comes from Portugal. Our native Marjoram is not so palatable as the foreign species and is seldom used. Tansy, *Tanacetum vulgare*, a very common wilding all over the country, was used to add flavour to puddings. Its dried leaves are an important ingredient in the preparation of insect destroying powders.

We have two Angelicas growing wild in this country. They are *Angelica archangelica* and *A. sylvestris*. It is questionable if the former, which is sometimes found in moist situations, is a native, but it has been cultivated in Britain for over four centuries. *A. sylvestris*, on the other hand, is an undoubted indigenous plant inhabiting many of our woodlands. There is no record of *A. sylvestris* being used for edible purposes, but the other was formerly grown for the goodness of its leaf-stalks. In these days they are sometimes candied and they have an agreeable flavour.

Coriander, *Coriandrum sativum*, is a doubtful native plant as we know that it was originally introduced from the East. It has, however, established itself as a wilding in some parts of the southern counties. It is grown for its tender leaves for use in salads and soups, but it is more generally cultivated on a large scale for its seeds which are used by confectioners and distillers to add flavour to many beverages. Another herb which is greatly used for the aromatic flavour of its seeds is the Caraway, *Carum Carvi*. It is very rare as a wild plant. Most people know the flavour of Caraway as

ROSEMARY
From John Parkinson's
Theatrum Botanicum, 1640

its seeds are so often used in cakes and confectionery. Camomile, *Anthemis nobilis*, is a wild perennial, and the whole plant is bitter and highly aromatic. It is a valuable herb, but is only grown for its importance in medicine. With it, for a similar purpose, we may group another perennial plant popularly called the Elecampane, botanically *Inula helenium*. It was largely grown at one time and was found in almost every village garden. The roots were candied and eaten as a confection; it was of more account as a purely medicinal plant and is used in the preparation of many drugs.

Rosemary, *Rosmarinus officinalis*, was introduced to our gardens from the shores and islands of the Mediterranean some time before the sixteenth century, and is thought to have been brought here by the Crusaders returning from the Holy Land. When the alchemists of the sixteenth century claimed that it had the power of stimulating the memory, its abstract qualities became more tangible than the older traditions associated with it, and it even became known as the "Herb of Memory." The plant is highly aromatic, and infusions of the leaves are made in some drinks. It is largely used in the manufacture of Hungary Water. Rosemary Conserve was another popular remedy for many ailments. Another equally popular aromatic garden plant is the Lavender, *Lavendula spica*, which was brought here from the South of Europe in 1658. It is seldom used in cookery but is greatly esteemed for its fragrance. Then we have the Thymes, old-fashioned shrublets that please everybody. The Common Thyme, *Thymus vulgaris*, came here from Spain and Italy in the sixteenth century. The Lemon Thyme, *T. citriodorus*, is distinguished by its golden foliage and strong smell of lemons. The leaves and tops of the thyme are used in soups, stuffings and sauces. Clary, *Salvia Sclarea*, from Italy, another sixteenth-century introduction, is used in soups. Sage, *Salvia officinalis*, from the South of Europe, is another favourite for soups and stuffings, and Tarragon, *Artemisia Dracunculus*, from Siberia, is another valuable aromatic plant much used in cookery.

FENNEL
From William Turner's *Herball*, 1562

GARDEN ANGELICA
From John Parkinson's *Theatrum Botanicum*, 1640

CONCLUSION

While living Herbs shall spring, profusely wild,
Or Garden cherish all that's sweet and gay;
So long thy works shall praise, dear Nature's child,
So long thy memory suffer no decay.

FINALLY, in these days when the art of horticulture has made such great progress and our knowledge of plant genetics has enabled our plant breeders to work in directions and by methods which ensure success, we can surely hope for a yet wider selection of vegetables and salads. When we consider, for example, what has been done with *Brassica oleracea*, we are encouraged to believe that some of our wild plants are capable of development. The material lies here in our own country, and only awaits the enterprise and skill of a plant breeder endowed with the necessary knowledge and patience.

Herbs, too, the "Simples" of our forefathers, laid the foundations of our modern gardens. They did much more. At one time the pharmacist had to rely solely upon herbs for his drugs and ointments, and apothecaries— the medicine men of old—had either to collect or grow their own material. In consequence, they became active and intelligent botanists. Two examples will suffice. John Gerarde, whose great *Herball* was published in 1597, was described as a Master in Chirurgerie, and he became a great and clever botanist. Then there was William Curtis (1746–1799) the founder of the *Flora*

Londinensis and the famous *Botanical Magazine* which, begun in 1787, is still published annually and is one of our most important horticultural journals. A complete set is the envy of every horticultural book collector. Curtis carried on business as a humble apothecary in Gracechurch Street, London, before he became a botanist.

CRUSHING HERBS IN A MORTAR
Woodcut from *Hortus Sanitatis*, 1491

A SHORT BIBLIOGRAPHY

The Herball, 1597 by John Gerarde.—*Theatrum Botanicum*, 1640 by John Parkinson.—*Encyclopeadia of Gardening*, 1822 by John C. Loudon.—*Memoirs*, 1824. Caledonian Horticultural Society.—*Vegetable Products of Scotland*, 1851 by Charles Lawson and Sons.—*Book of the Garden*, 1853 by Charles McIntosh.—*Origin of Cultivated Plants*, 1886 by De Candolle